THEY
SANG
A NEW
SONG

Stories of Great Hymns

THEY
SANG
A NEW
SONG

By Ruth MacKay
Illustrated by Gordon Laite

ABINGDON PRESS
New York   Nashville

Acknowledgments

To list all sources for a book like this would require numerous pages. I particularly am indebted, however, to the Chicago Public Library, the Newberry Library, and the *Chicago Tribune* library; to the Hymn Society of America; to the consuls of foreign countries; to government officials from Quebec to Oberndorf; and to my friends of various denominations.

I'd be remiss if I failed to mention the sympathetic interest of my husband, and the inspiration of the Rev. G. Carlton Story, Rector of the Church of the Mediator, Chicago, Illinois, where I became aware of the beauty and strength between the covers of a hymnal.

With such generous assistance I have hoped to add a small "grace note" to the music of the Christian church.

Ruth MacKay

Contents

"O sing unto the Lord a new song
for he hath done marvellous things."

Long ago, before there were hymns as we know them, way
back in the seventh century, men used to sing of valor. They
would gather for entertainment, and would pass around a harp
so each one could make up a song, all about warriors and heroic
deeds of adventure.

In one such gathering, a herdsman by the name of Caedmon
sat silent. When his turn came, he took the harp reluctantly, not
wishing to join in the entertainment.

But then he plucked the strings and began to sing about the
heroes of the Old Testament. He became very famous because he
was the first English Christian poet.

Caedmon sang a new song. Through many centuries, in many
lands, others sang unto the Lord a new song, and gave us our
heritage of hymns.

Have you ever wondered how?

The Bishop
Who Defied Kings

THOMAS KEN, 1637-1711

Old 100th
GENEVAN PSALTER, 1551

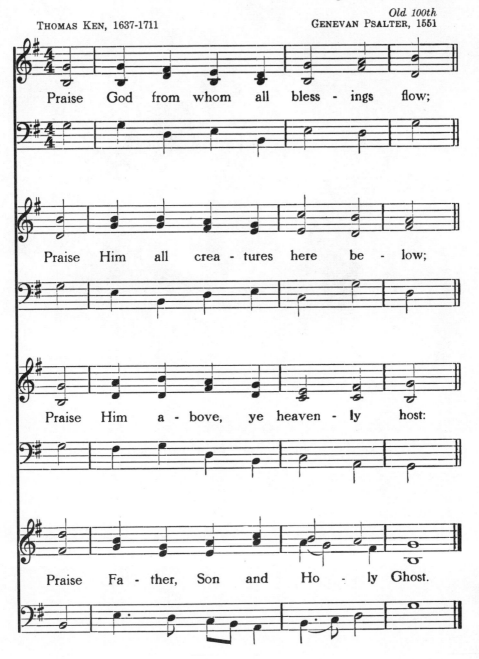

Praise God from whom all bless - ings flow;

Praise Him all crea - tures here be - low;

Praise Him a - bove, ye heaven - ly host:

Praise Fa - ther, Son and Ho - ly Ghost.

This story took place in England.

From England, the Pilgrims came to America. From England we get our language and much of our law. Many famous writers whose works we read, such as Shakespeare and Dickens, lived and wrote in England.

England is a monarchy; it is ruled by kings. At the time of our story, the 17th century, a king was powerful and to oppose him was very dangerous. In fact, it was a sure way of risking one's head!

But there are always brave men, and Thomas Ken was one of them. His boldness, it was said, was matched only by his conscience.

12

At an age when most children today are happy in kindergarten with their playmates, Thomas Ken knew sorrow. His mother died when he was five.

"Such a pity," said people in the peaceful English town of Little Berkhamstead. "He is such a bright boy!"

They spoke of his mother, who was the daughter of a poet and very scholarly. "With her gone," they said, "there seems to be no one to instruct the child."

"Lawyer Ken will work out something," replied others in the village. "He is not of a mind to let the education of his son suffer."

Education of young children in 1642 presented a problem. They couldn't be bundled off to the nearest grammar school, because among the villages there were only a few scattered schools, conducted by the clergy. Generally the parents, themselves, if they were well educated, instructed their children.

Those who had confidence in lawyer Ken were quite right in thinking he would figure out some plan. He arranged for Thomas to be taught by his much older half-sister, Ann.

Ann taught Thomas at home, and continued to do so even after she married Isaak Walton, the author of a famous book on fishing.

Mrs. Walton kept steadily at her task until the day came when Thomas was thirteen years old. Then he was ready to go away to Winchester, England, where there was a school for boys.

"I'm certain you are going to like this place," she said as she and Thomas arrived at Winchester. "Many of the boys plan to enter the service of the church, and they are fine lads.

"Look," she said, pointing out the magnificent cathedral. "It's the largest of its kind in all England. And just think, Thomas, in

13

the remains of the old castle you'll see the round table of King Arthur at which he used to sit surrounded by one hundred and fifty gallant knights! It's all quite exciting!"

The boy's face, which had been intensely serious until then, suddenly glowed with anticipation. Winchester *was* going to be an exciting place.

It was a blessing Thomas felt this way, because the very next

year after he entered school his father died and he was left without either one of his parents. But already he had learned to stand on his own feet and to be unafraid.

To further his education, he later attended the great Oxford University. And, like many of his Winchester schoolmates, he entered the ministry of the Church of England.

14

In time, he came back to Winchester, the school where he had been a student, to officiate at some of the church services. He stayed there several years, working on a manual of prayers and composing hymns for the students.

He reminded them, "It is a good thing to tell of the lovingkindness of the Lord early in the morning, and of his truth in the night season," and wrote morning and evening hymns for them. Our Doxology, "Praise God from Whom All Blessings Flow," was part of these hymns.

Thomas Ken enjoyed singing his morning and evening hymns accompanied by the spinet, a musical instrument in use before the modern piano, or by the viol, a stringed instrument rather like a violin and played with a bow. Often he said his joy would be greater in heaven if he could listen to his hymns "as sung by the faithful on earth."

Those quiet days with the students at Winchester passed all too quickly, and soon Thomas Ken assumed the responsibilities of a bishop, and also of chaplain to the king. Being chaplain to the king meant being his spiritual adviser throughout his lifetime, even to attending him on his deathbed.

King Charles II was a pleasure-loving monarch, often offending the people of England, and constantly in serious dispute with one group or another of his subjects. It was quite generally known that Bishop Ken objected to the king's misbehavior in his domestic life, and some thought Bishop Ken would suffer for it. Instead, the king secretly admired the plucky, forthright clergyman, and even was heard to remark, "I must go to church to let Bishop Ken tell me of my faults!"

But the next king of England, James II, looked with no such tolerance on any opposition. He threw Bishop Ken into the gloomy old Tower of London for refusing to read publicly a declaration he considered unfavorable to the church. He and six other bishops were imprisoned for two months.

However, the bishops were so popular that when they were brought to a jury trial (for disobedience to a royal command) they were declared not guilty. News that they were free spread quickly all over London. People lined the streets, kneeling and asking for a blessing as the bishops passed by. That night bonfires were lit and bells were rung in celebration, which didn't please the king in the palace one bit!

Once more Thomas Ken defied a king, but not with so fortunate an ending. James II was sent into exile, and William of Orange was made king. "William of Orange is not the rightful ruler," said Bishop Ken, "because King James is still alive although exiled from his people. Therefore, I cannot take the oath of allegiance to William!"

For this, the brave bishop lost his high position in the church. He was left with a small library, a little money, and a faithful school friend.

The days of kings, and royal commands to which he could not

conscientiously yield, were over in Bishop Ken's life. He shared his friend's home and continued to write religious poems, never dreaming that the beautiful four-line hymn of praise, written for the students of Winchester, might someday be more widely used in church services than anything except the Lord's Prayer.

Where Shepherds Watched on Christmas Eve

PHILLIPS BROOKS, 1835-1893

St. Louis
LEWIS H. REDNER, 1831-1908

O lit - tle town of Beth - le-hem, How still we see Thee lie!

A-bove Thy deep and dreamless sleep, the si - lent stars go by;

Yet in Thy dark streets shin - eth the ev - er - last - ing light,

The hopes and fears of all the years are met in Thee to-night.

A hundred years ago, American people didn't travel overseas as generally, nor as easily, as today.

There were no fast planes to fly them to Europe; there were no passenger jets to whisk them over vast distances in six or eight hours. A voyage from New York to a European port took twice as long as now, given good weather and a sturdy ocean liner.

It was on such a ship that a handsome six-foot-four American preacher, Phillips Brooks, set sail on Wednesday, August 9, 1865. Steamship "Scotia" had a smooth, good trip, with no storms on the way to Queenstown, Ireland.

Rev. Brooks wrote home that he "learned to love the sea for its greatness and gentleness, and for a certain calm beauty which took nothing from the grandeur."

This was the beginning of wonderful adventures for him. His church in Philadelphia had given him a year's leave of absence and during that time he went to many countries, including the Holy Land.

19

"It isn't a long distance to travel," thought Phillips Brooks, "only five or six miles. On horseback I should cover it in a couple of hours at most."

The young American preacher was visiting in Jerusalem, and now he was looking across to a lower hill beyond the city, and to Bethlehem.

The little town of Bethlehem was where David, the psalm-singer and king of the Old Testament, had lived as a boy. But more important, it was where Christ was born in a manger.

Rev. Brooks, on this Sunday, December 24, 1865, thought he would like to be on the fields where the shepherds had watched their flocks and the angel of the Lord had appeared to them. He wanted to be on that hallowed ground on Christmas Eve.

So he made arrangements for a horse to ride and started off.

Along the way he couldn't help noticing how different the winter in Palestine was from the New England winters he had known as a boy. Here the day wasn't bitter cold, though the air was brisk and pine scented. No snow lay on the ground, and the trees weren't bare and leafless. This was truly an "ever green" country.

The earth beneath the horse's hoofs was reddish. The sun felt warm on Rev. Brooks' head. " 'Tis December-June weather," he observed, and wrote this in a letter to his friends back home in the United States.

He wished his friends could be with him on this day-before-Christmas, particularly his young friends in the Philadelphia church. "They would love this!" he said to himself while he rode along.

As he turned over in his mind many recollections, he smiled to

think that when he was first out of college, he had believed himself a dismal failure because he couldn't keep order in a class of boys at the Boston Latin School. But now that he had become a preacher, he had no such worries. Young people were dear to his heart. And they know it, he thought happily, looking into a glowing sunset.

Before nightfall he reached Bethlehem. Until three in the morning, he attended church services. It was so memorable an experience that, a few weeks later, he took time from his travels to describe it in a letter to the boys and girls of his Trinity Church in Philadelphia.

"I do not mind telling you," he confessed in his letter, "though of course I should not like to have you speak of it to any of the older people of the church, that I am much afraid the younger part of my congregation has more than its share of my thoughts and interests. I can not tell you how many Sunday mornings since I left you I have seemed to stand in the midst of our crowded school-room . . . how many times I have heard our hymns ringing very strangely and sweetly through the music of some far-off country.

"I remember especially," he wrote, "on Christmas Eve when I was standing in the Old Church in Bethlehem, close to the spot where Jesus was born, how again it seemed as if I could hear voices that I know so well, telling each other of the 'Wonderful Night' of the Saviour's birth."

Three years later, back in Philadelphia, still remembering that very special Christmas Eve and the dark streets beneath the silent stars, still thinking of the children of his church, he wrote "O Little Town of Bethlehem." He asked the superintendent of the Sunday school, who also was the church organist, to compose music for it. It was sung during Christmas week, 1868.

Much that Phillips Brooks preached, and wrote, was published throughout the country. He became widely known and greatly admired. But today, his name is best known to many people because of the beauty of his Christmas hymn, "O Little Town of Bethlehem."

Then Give Us Something Better

St. Anne

ISAAC WATTS, 1674-1748

WILLIAM CROFT, 1678-1727

O God, our help in a - ges past,

Our hope for years to come,

Our shel - ter from the storm - y blast,

And our e - ter - nal home!

For a long time, families who went to church to worship together had just one kind of hymn. They sang only the psalms from the Old Testament.

A man, called the clerk, "lined out" the psalms to the congregation, which meant he gave out one line at a time. The people sang one line and then waited for the clerk to give out the next line. This went on for verse after verse and was often tiresome and dreary.

A lot of families must have twisted in the stiff, hard pews and wished they could have something different. Finally they did have. And all because of a pale, short-statured young man who, by expressing his opinion frankly, brought about a great change in hymn singing.

24

The Watts family was gathered for prayers. Enoch Watts, his head bowed, was leading the prayer. Suddenly small Isaac tittered, then hurriedly hushed.

After prayers, Enoch Watts said sharply, "Isaac, explain yourself. What do you mean by interrupting our devotions?"

The boy answered timidly, "I saw a mouse run up the bellrope by the fireplace and made up a rhyme. It goes this way:

> "A mouse for want of better stairs
> Ran up a rope to say his prayers."

Stern Enoch Watts was thoroughly displeased. Little Isaac, seeing his father's severe frown, cried:

> "O father, father, pity take
> And I will no more verses make."

Yet Isaac did make many more verses while still a young boy. His parents ran a boarding school in the city of Southampton, in England, and, to keep the students out of mischief, offered prizes for poems they wrote. Isaac composed a great number.

Later, as a young man of twenty-one, the same Isaac Watts stood before a group of older men. One of them was his father. All of them belonged to a church called "noncomformist" because it did not do things in the same way the established Church of England did.

"Why do you object to the singing in our meetinghouse, Isaac?" the older men wanted to know.

"I do not like always to sing the Old Testament psalms," he replied. "They were written for the people of that time. If we sing them, they should be written in the manner of our New Testament times. Besides, I think they should be more singable," he added earnestly.

The older men shook their heads doubtfully. Rhymed Old Testament psalms were the only hymns permitted in their church. But then, if the young man felt so strongly about it. . . .

"Very well, Isaac," they said at last, "give us something better."

Isaac Watts was only five feet tall, but he drew himself up to his full height. This was a challenge.

"I *will* give you something better," he promised.

26

The following Sunday in 1695, a new hymn, "Behold the Glories of the Lamb," was sung in the church. The next Sunday there was another new hymn, and the next, and the next.

For two whole years the church in Southampton had a new hymn every week. And every one of these hymns was written by Isaac Watts.

Soon it became clear that the young man with the slight build and the pale complexion was blessed with a rare gift for poetry, although he did not think so himself. "I make no pretenses to the name of a poet," he modestly remarked.

Yet, he wrote more than six hundred hymns, nearly all of them during the years of his early manhood. He set forth his ideas in simple form, seldom using long words. The poems which resulted were strong and appealing. Many were the psalms phrased in the language of the New Testament.

Most of his life was spent in writing. He knew Greek and Hebrew; he was a scholar and author of a number of books.

His collection of "Divine and Moral Songs for Children" found its way into countless households. And English-speaking children everywhere soon were memorizing his:

> "How doth the little busy bee
> Improve each shining hour;
> And gather honey all the day
> From every opening flower."

His music became popular in America as well as in England. The very first year Benjamin Franklin had a printing press, he published "Watts' Psalms and Hymns."

After Dr. Watts died, Sunday school children gave their pennies to erect a statue of him in the park at the end of Bar Street, in Southampton. And a monument was placed in Westminster Abbey, in London, in his honor because as a young man he so brilliantly answered the question: "Well, if you don't like what we're doing, can you give us something better?"

St. Francis, Brother of All Nature

ST. FRANCIS OF ASSISI, 1182-1226
Tr. WILLIAM H. DRAPER, 1855-1926

Lasst uns Erfreuen
From Geistliche Kirchengesang

All crea-tures of our God and King, Lift up your voice and with us sing Al - le - lu - ia! Al - le - lu - ia! Thou burn-ing sun with gold - en beam, Thou sil - ver moon with soft-er gleam: O praise Him, O praise Him, Al - le - lu - ia, Al - le - lu - ia, Al - le - lu - ia!

If you were to go to Italy, the sunny land of olive trees and vine-yards, you might visit Assisi, a very old town built on a hill in the Apennine Mountains.

There you'd be able to look down to the plain below and see the place where St. Francis worshiped in a little chapel. An Italian guide might point out to you that St. Francis and his followers lived in humble huts around the chapel down on the plain.

But most interesting would be the two churches built above St. Francis' tomb, quite unlike the churches you are accustomed to see, for one is an upper church and the other a lower church. In both of them you would feel surprisingly close to the beloved saint who was born over seven hundred years ago, because the walls are decorated with paintings that tell the story of his extraordinary life.

The paintings were done long ago by great masters of art. Some of them you may have seen in reproduction, especially the one of St. Francis surrounded by the birds he called his "little sisters."

For a long time, the Italian hill town of Assisi had buzzed with talk about Giovanni di Bernardone, more usually known as Francis because his father traveled often into France.

"Have you heard?" it was whispered from door to door. "'Tis said he gave a banquet for all his riotous young friends. They paraded through the streets, and crowned him king of the revels. . . ."

"Yes, but they say he broke away, and when the young noblemen found him, he was in a sort of daze and was completely changed. Now he cares nothing for fine clothes and gay singing, but devotes himself to the poor."

"Si! Si! But Pietro di Bernardone, it's rumored, is more angry than ever with his son. Poor Francis! He never did any real harm. He was young and a spendthrift, but he was always kind."

Neighbors and friends gazed fearfully upon the town's wealthy merchant, then, as he and his son Francis arrived to see the bishop of Assisi. Young Francis looked thin and worn.

The bishop cautiously closed a heavy door before permitting Pietro di Bernardone to speak.

"Monsignore," began the grim merchant, puffing with indignation, "I have taken my son before the city consuls in protest. He is throwing away his money, saying he must give to the poor. I asked that a civil document be drawn up to prevent his inheriting my money, whereupon my son announced he no longer was under civil authority since he had entered the service of God. So I have come to you because you are the religious authority. I have come. . . ."

The stout Pietro di Bernardone had to stop for breath.

"My friend," said the bishop quietly, "you must consider well what you are doing before you disinherit your son."

Young Francis stood silent as his father continued furiously, "My son has taken a colored drapery from my shop and sold it to get money to restore an old church. For that he hid in a cave, suspecting his father's wrath. Certainly things were bad enough when he was giving himself wholly to pleasure and extravagant living. But now with his idle talk about being commanded to repair God's house, I demand he be deprived of his share of my fortune."

Signor Bernardone patted the pocket of his waistcoat as though his money were hidden there.

Sadly the bishop began to prepare the document of disinheritance. And suddenly Francis, who was dressed in clothing suitable for the son of a rich merchant of the 13th century, began ripping off his garments. Putting about himself a cloak handed to him by the bishop, Francis cried out, "Hitherto I have called you my father on earth; henceforth I desire to say only 'Our Father who art in Heaven.'"

Without further words, Francis turned and fled into the hills beyond Assisi, leaving behind his home, his possessions, and the pleasures of his former life.

From then on, Francis gave himself to prayer and to the service of the sick and needy. In a short time he attracted followers who also pledged themselves to poverty and to helping the poor, the sick, and the suffering.

Shortly, when there were twelve such followers, the number of the disciples, they made a pilgrimage to Rome to see the pope and receive recognition for their small group. Francis was ap-

pointed their leader, and they went back to Assisi where they were given the use of a little chapel on the plain below the town.

They lived there in simple dwellings built of branches and twigs. Dressed like peasants in rough clothing, they worked in the fields to earn their daily bread.

From this small beginning grew a large and famous religious order, the Franciscans. It spread very rapidly and became so big and important that eventually Francis gave up the leadership, believing that his work was done and that there were others who could carry on his strenuous duties.

Throughout his last years he was very frail, but during this time he wrote the hymn, "All Creatures of Our God and King," expressing his joyous love of nature. He was so gentle there is a legend about the rosebushes which bloom by the old chapel. It is said they never have any thorns.

He regarded all creatures as his "brothers" or "sisters"—the birds, the deer, the field mice. Frequently he spoke of "Brother Sun" and "Sister Moon" and "Brother Wind" and "Sister Water," calling upon them to join him in worship of "our God."

Pikes Peak in a Prairie Wagon

KATHARINE LEE BATES, 1859-1929

Materna
SAMUEL A. WARD, 1847-1903

O beau - ti - ful   for   spa - cious skies, For   amb - er

waves   of   grain, For   pur - ple moun - tain   ma - jes - ties

A - bove   the   fruit - ed   plain!   A - mer - i - ca!   A-

mer - i - ca!   God   shed   His   grace   on   Thee.   And

crown Thy Good with Bro - ther-hood From sea   to   shin - ing   sea.

Pikes Peak, in Colorado, is not the highest in the long range of the Rocky Mountains, stretching through the western part of the United States. But Pikes Peak is perhaps the best known, and the one you hear most about.

It was named for Zebulon Pike, who discovered it in 1806. He was a colorful army officer, a daring young explorer, and—or so it was thought at one time—a highly secret spy for the American government.

Today we have none of his hazards of exploration if we wish to go up Pikes Peak. There is an automobile road and a cog railway to take us to the top, high above the line where the trees can grow, up where snowdrifts lie waiting for someone to make snowballs, even in August.

The immensity and beauty of the view, the miles and miles of grasslands sloping down from the foothills, takes everyone's breath away, as it did Katharine Bates'. She put her feelings into a patriotic hymn we all know. And here is how it happened.

36

"Shall we try the climb on foot, or on burros?" asked one of the more venturesome members of a group looking up at snowcapped Pikes Peak in the Rocky Mountains of Colorado.

"Oh, please, neither!" objected another, laughing. "This is supposed to be a carefree outing. Let's take an easier way."

Among those discussing the trip up the mountain was Katharine Lee Bates, a talented professor of English from Wellesley College, a woman's school in the East. Miss Bates had been an instructor at Colorado Springs that summer of 1893.

Classes were over, so she and some of the other teachers had decided to celebrate with an expedition to the snow-covered top of the mountain.

This was the high point of her summer which had also included a visit to the Chicago World's Fair, where she had been impressed by the glitter of an amusement park known as White City. It was her very first trip across the country to the West, and every mile of it had been interesting.

The thought of going up Pikes Peak was exhilarating to her, although she was thankful the climb on foot, or by burros, was finally ruled out.

Instead, the party set out in prairie wagons. These were covered farm wagons such as the early settlers had used to cross the prairies on their long trek West.

Everyone was in a gay mood. The dignified professors even laughed at the usual sign "Pikes Peak Or Bust" painted on the tailboard of each wagon. It was a slogan from the 1850's when easterners had rushed to Colorado in search of gold and silver.

Horses laboriously pulled them to the halfway house. Here,

according to Miss Bates' own story, "the horses were replaced by mules." On and up they went.

"We were hoping," she said, "for half an hour on the summit." But the high altitude was too much for two members of the party. They became faint, and so, Miss Bates recalled, "we were bundled into the wagons again, and started on our downward plunge so speedily that our sojourn on the peak remained in memory hardly more than one ecstatic gaze."

Afterwards, Miss Bates remembered the all-too-short moment on Pikes Peak and said, "It was then and there, as I was looking out over the sea-like expanse of fertile country spreading away so far under those ample skies, that the opening lines of the hymn, 'America the Beautiful' floated into my mind."

It was not too long after this that her summer trip came to an end. And shortly the fall semester at Wellesley College was in full swing with studious young women in high-necked white shirt-

39

waists and long black skirts filing into Miss Bates' classrooms.

But tucked away in her notebook, with other jottings of her summer vacation, were four stanzas of "America the Beautiful."

She just plain forgot about them for two whole years! Then, on a sudden impulse, she copied them and sent them to a magazine called *The Congregationalist*. Instantly, people everywhere liked them and asked for permission to set them to music so they could sing the inspiring words.

The one brief, beautiful gaze from Pikes Peak had given the American people a patriotic hymn to be sung in schools and churches, and by boy scouts, girl scouts, camp fire girls, soldiers, and sailors on national holidays, and in welcome to strangers from distant lands. It has been sung even in Canada as "O Canada the Beautiful," and in Mexico, as "Mi Mejico."

Sometimes, to Miss Bates' astonishment, the words were sung all wrong; the beginning of the fourth stanza, "O beautiful for patriot dream," for example, once came out "O beautiful for patriot drum!" But she accepted such thoughtless mistreatment of her splendid hymn cheerfully. She was happy, she said, that the American people had adopted it, showing that they had deep faith in the brotherhood of man.

The Major's Daughter
from County Tyrone

CECIL F. ALEXANDER, 1823-1895

Dundee (*Windsor*)
From ESTES PSALTER, 1592

There is a green hill far a - way,

With - out a cit - y wall,

Where the dear Lord was cru - ci - fied,

Who died to save us all.

The boys and girls of Ireland live in a country where the grass is such a brilliant green it is called "The Emerald Isle." They have fresh, fair complexions, and bright red cheeks, and they speak with an Irish brogue.

In the northern part of Ireland, you'll find County Tyrone.

County Tyrone, in the year 1848, was a serene place where people devoted themselves to the weaving of fine linens and to agriculture. Stolid plow horses made furrows in the soil where invading armies once had been on the run before the war cries of the fighting chieftain, Shane O'Neill.

Sunday, a hundred years ago, was a rather long day for the boys and girls who lived in the town of Strabane, of County Tyrone, in northern Ireland. There wasn't much they could do to amuse themselves and still keep the Sabbath as they were taught they should.

Sunday afternoons they could walk to the edge of the river Mourne, or climb the grassy hills, or stroll past green fields where cattle grazed peacefully.

In contrast to the scenes of tranquillity around them, the young folks would tell each other, as they walked, hair-raising tales handed down for generations in their families. These were blood-curdling stories of the days when County Tyrone rang with the battle cry of conquering O'Neill, when shields and flashing swords gleamed in the sunlight.

"My grandmother," one lad liked to recall, "used to say even the deer and the eagles would flee, frightened by the fearless warriors!"

On Sunday mornings the boys and girls of Strabane attended church to learn the doctrines of their faith.

And of this they talked also. "Others may know what the Catechism be meaning," said Barney, a rosy-cheeked, blue-eyed youth. "It's me, myself, that will never learn. Now what would be the Holy Ghost if not something to make tremble the bravest soul?"

"Och, Barney," exclaimed Kitty, an Irish colleen with a mouth like a cherry. "I'm thinking you sat too close to the dimpled Maurine when our teacher was explaining this!"

The boy blushed as Kitty continued, "The Holy Ghost is none other than our most Holy God, our Father in Heaven, who speaks to our hearts and tells us what is right for us to be doing. And he comforts those who sorrow. Our teacher, Miss Humphreys, told us all about it."

The Apostles' Creed, the Ten Commandments, and the Lord's Prayer all contained sentences boys and girls, then as now, found hard to understand.

Happily for them, a certain Major Humphreys of the Royal Marines lived in County Tyrone. He had a daughter by the name of Cecil Frances who taught in the Sunday school.

Cecil Frances possessed a real talent for poetry. She had another talent, too, a wonderful understanding of what puzzled her pupils.

So she wrote poems and hymns for her Sunday school class. In all, she wrote approximately four hundred hymns and generously presented her earnings from them to a school for deaf and dumb children.

One day she was jogging along in a light carriage on her way to the market. The children of her Sunday school class were worrying her. Part of the Apostles' Creed, "Suffered under Pontius Pilate, was crucified, dead, and buried," distressed her boys and girls. "Why did one who was so pure and good and gentle have to suffer?" they asked her.

She had tried to explain. "Christ's gift," she said, "was one of supreme love. When he died, he gave all mankind the glorious hope that there is much, much more to life than our short stay on earth. His was the most loving sacrifice of all. In return, we must love him, too, and try to live the way he taught us while he walked this earth."

She thought this over on the way to the market, and as she passed

a hill which she imagined may have been like the one where Christ died, some lines came into her mind. She began to write a hymn to interpret Christ's death to young people: "There Is a Green Hill Far Away."

Quite soon afterwards she was married in the church at Strabane to Rev. William Alexander, a promising Irish clergyman who later held high offices in the church.

Pressed on every side by household tasks and duties connected with her husband's work, she continued to write. And she never forgot the boys and girls of County Tyrone.

In the preface of one of her books of poetry, she said, "May this volume tend to make Sunday a pleasant day to children. May it help to teach them to praise God, the Father, Son, and Spirit, to understand the Bible, and through this fair creation, to look up to him who is its creator."

Palestrina, Prince of Music

Symphonia Sirenum, Cologne 1695
Tr. Francis Pott, 1832-1909

Victory
Giovanni P. Da Palestrina, 1525-1594

The strife is o'er, the bat - tle done;

The vic - to - ry of life is won;

The song of tri - umph has be - gun.

Al - le - lu - ia!

The age in which we are living seems very important and exciting to us. Parents and children talk about planets and missiles and the chance of going to the moon. In their dinner-table conversation, they touch on innumerable subjects unknown to past generations.

Yet there have been other periods of history quite as exciting as ours. One of these covered about two centuries and was called the Renaissance, a French word meaning "rebirth."

The Renaissance was a time when the people of Europe discovered, all over again, the joy of being alive. They surrounded themselves with as many rich and beautiful things as they could—paintings, sculpture, magnificent buildings, and the delicate craft of goldsmiths.

Great artists in countries such as Italy were favored and honored, and thus were encouraged to do their finest work. Some of them had several skills. Michelangelo was a sculptor, a painter, an architect, an engineer, and a poet. And Cellini, the wonderful metalworker, carved statues and wrote a remarkable book.

The Renaissance, in Italy, was a time when everyone wanted to live in a palace like a prince.

This story is about a different kind of prince.

48

His name actually wasn't Palestrina. It was Giovanni Pierluigi da Palestrina, which meant that he was the son of the well-to-do Pierluigi family of the Italian town of Palestrina. As time went on and he became very famous, he dropped the first part of his name and was called Palestrina for the place of his birth.

But in his childhood and youth he was Giovanni to his family and neighbors in the ancient, picturesque hill town. His mother told him it was originally called Praeneste, the place of cool and fragrant breeze. "And so it is, my son," she said, "and so it has been for the many generations your ancestors have lived here."

Twice, as a small boy, he left the little town of Palestrina and, with his parents' permission, traveled twenty miles to the great city of Rome, which then was the cultural center of the world.

Once he rode, seated on a horse behind a good-natured serving man, and stayed on the outskirts of Rome in a small inn that his grandmother, Jocobella Pierluigi, had owned.

Another time—and this was most thrilling of all—Giovanni was allowed to travel with the bishop and all his attendants when they went to visit the pope. He crept into a great high-vaulted church and heard the mass and all the beautiful music accompanying the prayers and ceremonies of the church.

He wasn't sure which he loved most, his own country town of Palestrina or the exciting city of Rome. When the chance came, the year he was twelve, for him to go to Rome to be in the choir of one of the large churches, he wanted to accept. On the other hand, he couldn't bear to leave his home at the foot of the Sabine hills.

"I'm afraid I'll miss the garden back of our house, and the town gates and the fountains," he said wistfully to his two brothers. "In Rome there won't be the shepherds in their wide cloaks and high-crowned hats! And, there'll not be water-carriers with their copper pots! I'll miss all these, and you, too, Silla and Bernadino."

"Oh, come now," interrupted Bernadino, hoping to cheer his brother, "at least you'll not miss Palma, for never have I seen another brother and sister who argued so furiously!"

In the end, Giovanni and his mother and father agreed that he should become a chorister in Rome. He stayed there four worthwhile years. Then when his voice had grown too deep for a boys' choir, he was happy to return to Palestrina, to the lovely landscape and the old, familiar ruins. This was in 1540; he was sixteen.

In a few years, because he loved and knew music, he was invited to be the organist and choirmaster in his church in Palestrina.

He went to work to train the young voices and teach the choir all he had learned in Rome, devoting long hours to choir practice and to the organ. This pleased the new bishop of the town, who sometimes dropped in to hear the music.

Not long after, the head of the Catholic church, whose residence was in Rome, died; and the bishop of Palestrina became the new head, as Pope Julius III. He sent for Giovanni and asked him to teach the boys in the choir at the new and lofty basilica of St. Peter's, the largest church in the entire Christian world.

By now, Giovanna, called Palestrina, was a young man eager to join his talents with other artists of the Renaissance. He began to write superb music, masses for the church, which he published at his own expense.

Occasionally he caught fleeting glimpses of the tall, aging

figure of Michelangelo in his black satin doublet. It was the same Michelangelo who had decorated the ceiling of the Sistine chapel with magnificent scenes from the Old Testament.

No greater dream could have come true for the young Palestrina, still in his twenties, than to be in such a creative atmosphere. Only, like most dreams, it didn't last. Through no fault of his own, he had to give up his fine position. Sad and disappointed, he left Rome for a while.

Yet there was no writer of religious music to take his place, and eventually the dignitaries high in the church realized this. They were not satisfied with the kind of music they were receiving, and they needed Palestrina. "Come back," they urged him. "Come back and simplify and purify our music."

This he did. His compositions spread to many countries and today are heard throughout the world. The music for our Easter hymn, "The Strife Is O'er," was adapted from his writings to accompany the stirring words of an unknown author.

Palestrina became the head of a school of music. The former

boy-genius from the Sabine hills was hailed by his students as "the ocean toward which all streams flow."

And, in the last fading days of the Renaissance in Italy, he was buried with the noble title, "Prince of Music."

From A to Z
in a Day

CHARLES WESLEY, 1707-1788

ROWLAND H. PRICHARD, 1811-1887

Hyfrydol

1. Come, Thou long-ex-pect-ed Je-sus, Born to
2. From our fears and sins re-lease us: Let us

set Thy peo-ple free;
find our rest in Thee.
Is-rael's strength and

con-so-la-tion, Hope of all the earth Thou

art. Dear De-sire of ev-ery na-tion,

Joy of ev-ery long-ing heart.

In some ways, Susannah Wesley was a surprisingly modern mother, for she managed her large family with a well-organized routine. Her children were bathed at regular times and put to bed at regular hours. They were fed on schedule.

She systematically taught her children and wrote three books on religion for them. She kept a diary. One entry in it said: "On Monday I talk with Molly; on Tuesday with Hetty; Wednesday with Nancy; Thursday with Jackie; Friday with Patty; Saturday with Charles; and with Emily and Subey together on Sunday." Even her private conversations with her children were planned for and held in orderly fashion.

Life back in the early 1700's moved along at a lively pace in the big old rectory at Epworth, England. Of the many children in the family, two were especially close to each other all their lives, Charles and John.

"Happy birthday, Charles!" called his older brother, John, on December 18, 1712, as the Wesley household wakened to a busy day.

Every day was busy in the big family. Mother Wesley had many children to feed, bathe, and instruct. Father Wesley had family prayers and, in addition, his church duties in the tiny village of Epworth, England, where he was the rector.

But this was not an ordinary day, for it was Charles' fifth birthday.

Charles was the eighteenth child of the Wesleys. And, just as it had been for his brothers and sisters, his fifth birthday was set apart by his mother for him to learn the alphabet.

"By sundown," promised John, three and a half years older, "you'll know your letters, as I did, from *A* to *Z*. Tomorrow you'll be given the first sentence of the Bible to read: 'In the beginning God created the heaven and the earth.' "

However, even before this, Mrs. Wesley had begun to teach little Charles about God and religion. Sometimes she instructed her children as though they were a class in a schoolroom. When she divided the days of the week among them to talk privately with them, Saturday was Charles' day with his mother. But this week, Thursday—his birthday—was the important day.

Exactly as John had said, early in the morning Charles set about learning the alphabet. *A, B, C, D, E, F, G, H, I, J, K, L, M.* By noon, half of the alphabet was learned. And just as John had promised, by sundown Charles knew his letters through to *Z*.

The next morning the big family Bible was opened. Charles' small finger traced the first line in it until he was sure he could

read it and say the letters of each word, starting with "In the beginning . . ."

In the days following that birthday, the alphabet proved to be a wonderful gift. It was like a golden key that unlocked all the books of the Bible. Charles read and read. He read about Noah and how he let a dove out a window of the ark to see if there was dry land where the dove could light.

Charles read about Moses and how the Egyptian princess found him, a babe in the bullrushes, on the river Nile. The little boy in the parsonage at Epworth learned all about the kings of Egypt, and about wise King Solomon. And he learned about Elisha and the chariots of fire.

The child's head fairly burst with stories that made him marvel and lie awake at night imagining that he, too, lived in those long-ago Old Testament days.

He talked this over with John who, because he was a little older, seemed to know a great deal. The two boys were the best of friends. They had fun together, even though the Wesleys were always poor. And they had their excitement, too!

About the time Charles was twelve, the family strongly believed their house was haunted by a ghost. A most extraordinary ghost, it not only rattled windows and moved dishes, but appeared in the form of a four-legged animal wearing a nightgown. The boys nick-named him "Old Jeffery."

Charles and John attended the same college in England, Oxford, where Charles formed "The Holy Club" of which John became the head.

As Charles explained it, "I went to the weekly sacrament and persuaded two or three young students to accompany me, and to observe the method of study prescribed by the University. This gained me the harmless name of Methodist."

After they were graduated from college, the brothers sailed for America. For a time they stayed in Georgia. Charles was secretary to the founder of the colony, General Oglethorpe, and John preached to the Indians.

More truthfully, he *tried* to preach to the Indians. But John didn't know the language of the tribes. He was completely confounded by something like this:

Kesuk kukootumushteaumoo
God wussohsumoonk
Mamahehekusuk
Wumahtuhkon
Wutanakausnonk

which was the first verse of the Nineteenth Psalm: "The heavens declare the glory of God; and the firmament sheweth his handy-work."

Meanwhile, Charles was having trouble with the governor. So, before long the two brothers left the New World and went back to their homeland.

In England again, they began preaching in small villages. Each of the brothers traveled many miles. Charles galloped on horse-back throughout the west of England, Wales, and Ireland.

And while he traveled, he wrote hymns. He must have turned out almost one a day for months, even years. In all, he wrote more than six thousand hymns, most of them while riding over the

countryside, the words coming to him to the "clop-clop" of the horse's hoofs.

Many of his hymns were included in books which he and John published together for Methodist chapels they established. Singing in the chapels was carried on without any musical instrument.

Lack of an organ didn't spoil the zest of the congregation in John's London chapel, once an old foundry. Here he led his people in singing the hymns of his brother.

"Charles," he declared, "is one of the best poets. His hymns show the purity, the strength, and the eloquence of the English language."

This is the language little Charles began to master on his fifth birthday with the family Bible before him. His hymn for Advent, "Come, Thou Long Expected Jesus," tells the Old Testament story of the people of Israel and their long wait for the promise of Christ's birth to be fulfilled.

When the Organ Broke Down

Joseph Mohr, 1792-1848

Stille Nacht
Franz Gruber, 1787-1863

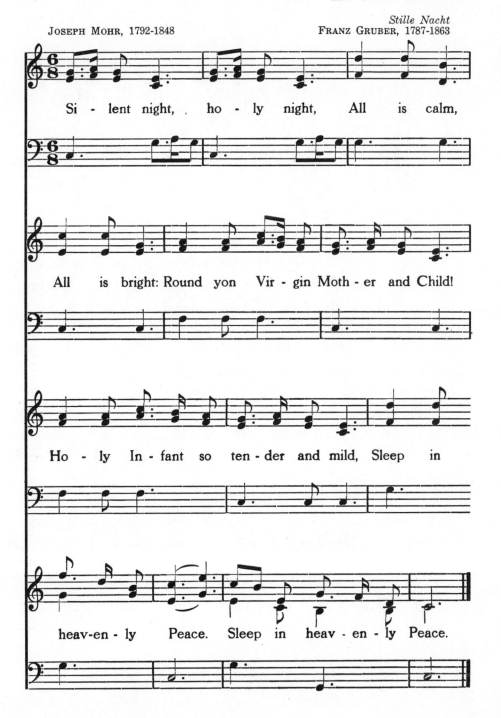

Si - lent night, ho - ly night, All is calm,

All is bright: Round yon Vir - gin Moth - er and Child!

Ho - ly In - fant so ten - der and mild, Sleep in

heav-en - ly Peace. Sleep in heav - en - ly Peace.

Oberndorf Church

Comparatively few of the hymns we sing today are set to the original melody. Many of them were sung for a long time to tunes the people knew, folk melodies that had been handed down from generation to generation.

This fitting of words to a melody sometimes brought about curious situations. When the Pilgrims landed in America, they only knew three or four melodies. They sang all their hymns to one or the other of these melodies without any organ accompaniment. Quite often the members of the congregation in the same church, singing at the same time, singing the same words, weren't singing the same melody. The result was a fearful din!

Up to the beginning of the 18th century in America, such discord in church singing was pretty general. One minister complained, "It sounded like five hundred different tunes roared out at the same time!"

But no confusion has ever existed over the Christmas carol, "Silent Night," because, on a certain frosty December day, the verse and the music were created to go beautifully together.

62

There was the sound of feet crunching along in the snow; then came a rap on the door, and the door was flung open.

"Joseph Mohr! What are you doing here? Have you walked this distance from Oberndorf on such a wintry day? If you catch a cold in the throat, what will we do for Christmas Eve services tonight? It is bad enough that the organ is out of order!"

"Ach, Franz, just because you are a respected choir leader, and an organist besides, you do not know everything."

Joseph Mohr laid his hand on his friend's shoulder. " 'Tis about the organ I'm most troubled, for there is no chance we can use it."

Father Mohr, the young assistant priest of St. Nicholas Church in Oberndorf, shed his heavy coat, and sat down by the fire in the simple dwelling of Franz Gruber.

"And this is why I'm here," the priest continued, reaching in his pocket for a folded sheet of paper. "Read this. It's a poem I've just finished. Now, if you could give it a musical setting, we could sing it tonight."

"As you know," he went on earnestly, "our people will come as always from miles around, on frozen paths through the hills, just to attend the service in our little parish church on Christmas Eve. I am not willing that we should disappoint them because we do not have the music they love."

Franz Gruber's hand shook as he began to read the words his friend had written. "Good! Good!" he exclaimed excitedly in German.

He began to hum, then stopped. "Yes! Yes, Joseph! I'll write the music. It could be for two solo voices and a guitar. You can sing the tenor part. I'll sing the bass, and accompany us on the guitar." His face was flushed with eagerness. "Then," he continued, "perhaps we might have one or two members of the choir join in the final refrain of each verse."

The moment Joseph Mohr's footsteps on the snow died away in the distance, Franz Gruber began jotting down the notes as they came to him. And on that Christmas Eve in 1818, "Silent Night, Holy Night" was sung for the first time in the church of St. Nicholas, in the Austrian village of Oberndorf, just off the main road which leads to the big city of Salzburg.

The world might never have known about "Silent Night, Holy Night" had not the organ builder who came to repair the church organ copied down the song. As he traveled from village to village, and from city to city, he taught it to people he met. Among

these were four sisters, glove-makers by trade. To earn extra money, they sang at village fairs.

They liked the song, and wherever they went, they sang it. Because they sang it mainly in that part of Austria known as the Tyrol, "Silent Night, Holy Night" became famous as a Tyrolean folk song.

It grew extremely popular, spread to other countries, and was translated into several languages. Nevertheless, no one knew where the song had come from or who had composed it.

At last, after many years, somebody took the trouble to find out. The royal court musicians in Berlin wrote to the Cathedral at Salzburg and asked if anyone knew about it.

It just happened that the son of Franz Gruber was a choirboy in the Cathedral. He was certain his father had composed the music and could supply all the information. The boy got in touch with his father.

Franz Gruber sat down and wrote a letter to the royal court musicians, containing a statement of the circumstances under which "Silent Night, Holy Night" had been written for a village church.

Today on Christmas it is sung in places far distant from Oberndorf. And on each Christmas Eve it is sung faithfully in the Austrian village where portraits of Franz Gruber and Joseph Mohr are now lastingly carved in stone.

A Quaker Boy
in a Lonely Farmhouse

JOHN G. WHITTIER, 1807-1892

FREDERICK C. MAKER, 1844-1927

Rest

Dear Lord and Fa - ther of man - kind, For-
give our fool - ish ways; Re - clothe us in our
right - ful mind, In pur - er lives Thy
serv - ice find, In deep - er rev - erence, praise.

The Quakers belong to a religious group called the Society of Friends. They were nicknamed Quakers because one of their leaders once told a judge he should "quake before the Lord." At first the term Quakers was used in ridicule, but after a while it became the popular name for these God-fearing, conscientious people.

There were several settlements of Quakers in the early days of the United States. William Penn, the founder of Pennsylvania, was a Quaker.

The Quakers were people who lived very simply. Their houses and their meetinghouses were plain. Their clothes were plain, too, for they didn't believe in luxury or display of any sort.

The Quakers considered all men and women equal, and addressed everyone as "thee." They were peaceful and against war.

They brought up their children to be obedient and kind. When families went to church they sat very still, amid silence, because they did not believe a preacher or preaching was necessary. Instead, they were taught that each person is given an "inward light" by the Holy Ghost, to guide his actions.

Consequently, they attended church to receive this inner guidance in quiet, trustful meditation.

In such a setting, a little Quaker boy lived a hundred years ago.

The boy, straight as an arrow, ran down to the bridle post just at the left of the gate to meet the peddler on his rounds of the villages.

"Thee never has many books in thy sack," said John Greenleaf Whittier, speaking in the language of his Quaker parents. The peddler lowered his sack to the ground, and young John began poking around among its contents—pots and pans, and herbs for curing rheumatism.

"Here," said the peddler, holding up a worn brown book. "This should make fine reading for a lad of your age, although the Scotch poet, Robert Burns, doesn't use the 'thee's' and 'thou's' of you Quakers. He has his own style of writing."

The peddler turned the pages. "Listen to this: 'My heart is sair—I dar na tell . . .' Now why couldn't he say his heart is sore and he dassn't tell?"

John didn't seem to be hearing.

"If the price is not too high, I'll buy it," he said solemnly. And the book was bought.

Although it was a bit tattered in the beginning, it became more so through the winter evenings in the lonely farmhouse near Haverhill, Massachusetts. John read every page until he knew it by heart.

And while he tramped through the fields, a "barefoot boy with cheeks of tan" (as he later described himself), he began to make up verses of his own.

When he was nineteen, he wrote his first real poem and sent it, without his name, to the weekly newspaper.

The days were unbearably long as he waited from week to

week to see if his poem would be published. He scarcely dared hope it would be.

At last, one morning while John was mending a stone fence, the postman tossed the newspaper from his leather bag. John bent down to pick it up, and there, in print, was his poem.

His delight was almost more than he could stand. He could hardly believe it! After that, he sent poems regularly to the editor, and regularly they were printed, until the publisher grew curious about his unknown poet and asked the postman who it could be.

"Must be the son of Quaker Whycher," volunteered the postman. "The boy's had little enough schooling; but he's always writing when he's not farming or mending his shoes at their cobbler's bench."

This made the publisher even more curious. So he rode to the

Whittier home, some miles away. He had heard that John was of a silent, brooding nature, but religious and sensitive to beauty, and he wanted to see for himself.

"I trust thy errand is a good one," said John's mother, answering the door in her severe gray Quaker dress with a white kerchief folded at her throat. "I'll fetch my son."

John was out in the fields. He came in the back door, stopping in the kitchen to wash his hands and face, and to comb his hair. Then he walked into the parlor, a shy, slender young man.

The stranger was standing, holding his wide-brimmed, high-crowned hat in his hand.

"I have been publishing your poems," he said, "and have taken this trip of several miles to advise you to improve your talents. You should be attending Haverhill Academy."

Just then farmer Whittier entered the room and overheard what was being said.

"We have a farm to be worked; thee must not put ideas in the boy's head which unfit him for his duties here."

The publisher's face was serious. "John's ideas," he answered gravely, "will make this farm famous some day."

The publisher's prophecy proved true. In later years John Greenleaf Whittier's poems brought vivid pictures of New England farm life to thousands of readers.

Although some time afterwards his father relented and sent John to Haverhill Academy, he really had little education. He lived nearly all his eighty-five years close to the place where he was born, much of the time in Amesbury where his family moved to be nearer the little white meetinghouse of the Society of Friends.

71

Great writers and statesmen became his friends. His constant companion, however, was a ridiculous parrot called Charlie. Charlie had the run of the house. Before he came to live with the Whittiers, he had been with rough people whose language was not to the liking of the Quaker poet. So he taught the bird to use gentle words like "thee" and "thou."

Charlie, unfortunately, never quite forgot his earlier teaching. One Sunday morning as the people of Amesbury were passing the house on their way to church, Charlie got up on the roof and began using all the forbidden words.

The churchgoers were shocked. As the mischievous Charlie was removed from the roof, repeating his favorite phrase, "What does Charlie want? . . . . What does Charlie want?" the serene eyes of Mr. Whittier twinkled.

"Thou worldly little creature," he remonstrated, "what Charlie wants is to behave in unbecoming manner for a good Friends' household!"

In that good Friends' household, Mr. Whittier, working in his study surrounded by books, wrote many poems which expressed the peacefulness and trust of the Quakers. From one of his long poems, the lines were taken for the hymn "Dear Lord and Father of Mankind."

Nightfall
in a Mining Town

SABINE BARING-GOULD, 1834-1924   *Merrial*
JOSEPH BARNBY, 1838-1896

Now the day is o - ver,

Night is draw - ing nigh,

Shad - ows of the eve - ning

Steal a - cross the sky.

Some famous persons are remembered long after their deaths because of the entire records of their lives. Now and then, however, we find someone whose name becomes a household word for just one dramatic incident.

For example, we all know about John Alden because he tried to further the romantic hopes of his friend, Miles Standish, and was told by a young Puritan miss, "Speak for yourself, John." Every school child has heard about Betsy Ross because it is believed that she made the first American flag.

The same thing is true of the authors of our great hymns. Some of them became famous for writing only one beautiful poem which was set to music, and which people have sung in their churches for generations. A single hymn made the writer illustrious.

There are other poets of the church who gained renown for any number of things they did. One such hymn-writer, Sabine Baring-Gould, was the author of so many books on so many different subjects that they crowded the library shelves of England.

75

"You'll jolly well find this different from what you're used to," remarked a young chap carrying three heavy suitcases. Then for a moment he was covered with confusion, for the person to whom he was speaking so familiarly had just arrived at the village of Horbury to be the new curate. Rev. Baring-Gould was a mannerly gentleman and one to be treated with respect.

But the newcomer smiled in warm response to the boy's outburst, so the lad went on to explain. "You see, sir, ours is a mill town where wool and other kinds of cloth are manufactured. Besides, we are in the coal-mining district of Yorkshire. Our people are hard-laboring and poor, and not educated as you are."

The boy set down the curate's suitcases on the doorsill as Sabine Baring-Gould looked about him.

"I think I'm going to like it here," he said thoughtfully.

Life in Horbury *was* different from the life Rev. Baring-Gould had lived for his thirty years till then. He had been born in the south of England in a city high above the river Exe. The cathedral he had known as a boy had massive Norman towers; and inside the cathedral he had once looked with awe and wonder at the great oak throne of the bishops.

Sabine Baring-Gould was the oldest son of a country squire who owned a big estate of three thousand acres. Sabine's grandparents and great-grandparents had lived on the same estate.

Before entering the ministry, he had studied at one of the finest universities in all England, and he had traveled in France and in Germany. Horbury was his first curacy.

He unpacked his suitcases and arranged his belongings. As the day wore on, he saw the workers coming from the mills, carrying their empty lunch pails, tired after long hours at their work.

He was distressed to notice that some of them were very young. His only comfort was that things were better than they had been when small children were put to work in dark mines and in mills, and Sunday schools were opened to teach them during their one day of rest.

He stood a long time at his window and watched the stream of workers as they passed his house on their way home.

"Soon they'll be sitting around big tables in their kitchens, having a good, hot supper. They'll be cheerful, as these people always are," he told himself. And again he thought, I'm going to like it here.

He most certainly did. He even found a wife among the pretty

77

mill hands. Her name was Grace Taylor. She was sixteen when he fell in love with her. In order to educate her to be a proper wife for a clergyman of his standing, he sent her away for instruction. Then, before long, they were married in a simple village church. They lived happily together for nearly half a century.

While he was at Horbury, the children were his great interest; in particular, the boys and girls at a mission in the town. He wrote two hymns especially for them.

One was the marching song, "Onward, Christian Soldiers," written for a children's processional to a neighboring village. The other was taken from a verse in the Bible: "When thou liest down, thou shalt not be afraid; yea, thou shalt lie down, and thy sleep shall be sweet." He put this reassuring thought into a hymn for young people, "Now the Day Is Over." One stanza, seldom sung, reads:

"Now the darkness gathers,
　Stars begin to peep,
　Birds and beasts and flowers
　Soon will be asleep."

When his father died, Rev. Baring-Gould went back to his family's estate in south England. He divided his time between the people of his parish, all of whom he knew and loved, and quiet hours in his study. He wrote books on history and travel and folk-lore, a fifteen-volume "Lives of the Saints," and many popular novels. There were ninety-three books in all. And he wrote a few more hymns, but his best known ones were inspired by the children of the mission in Horbury.

The Voyage of a Black-robed Giant

JEAN DE BREBEUF, 1642
Tr. J. E. MIDDLETON

French Melody

'Twas in the moon of win - ter time when all the birds had

fled, That Might - y Git - chi Man - i - tou sent

an - gel choirs in-stead. Be - fore their light the stars grew dim,

And wan-d'ring hunters heard the hymn: "Je - sus, your King, is born;

Je - sus is born; In ex - cel - sis glo - ri - a!"

When the white man came to North America, the Redskins were already here. There were numerous tribes of Indians, some more civilized than others. Most of them were savages engaged in tribal warfare, and ruled by weird, often cruel, superstitions.

From the white traders, the Indians learned to bargain for beads and ornaments in exchange for beaver or moose skins. But it was from the early missionaries that many Indian tribes first learned about the Christian God. Jean De Brebeuf was one of these missionaries. A French Jesuit priest, he arrived in Quebec, Canada, in June, 1625.

Father Jean, with giant steps, strode down to the bank of the mighty St. Lawrence River where partly loaded canoes lay in the sunshine. With joy he knew that at last the longed-for day had dawned. He was about to leave for Huronia, to establish his first mission among the Huron Indians. It was for this he had left his homeland and crossed the ocean, had abandoned his position as treasurer in a French college, and had traveled to a strange wilderness called New France. And it was for this he had spent a full year of waiting in Quebec.

The only way he could make the trip was by canoe, and by agreement of the Hurons to take him and his two companions on the thousand-mile journey to the distant country. Rich gifts had been offered and had finally been accepted by the Indians. They were now packed into canoes along with the missionaries' supplies of warm clothing, blankets, kettles, and knives.

Suddenly, as Father Jean prepared to go, a murmur of protest arose. "Echon," the Indians said, using their own pronunciation for *Jean*, "you are too large for our canoes. They will tip over. All will be drowned. No, no. We cannot take you."

"I know I am a great bull of a man," replied the big Jesuit missionary, joking because his last name, in French, meant "beef." "But take this hatchet. 'Twill cut down trees taller than I."

The extra gift had no effect. Instead, the Hurons eyed him from head to toe. "A black-robed giant," they told one another, as Father Jean stood erect in his long black Jesuit robe and wide-brimmed black hat. "He may be a sorcerer!" And off they paddled, after depositing the gifts and blankets and kettles, and the good priest himself upon the shore.

81

He was looking sadly after them when another Indian chief appeared and boasted that he owned a much larger canoe, sufficient for a half dozen men or more. It was surely big enough for "Echon," if his gifts were as ample as himself!

Father Jean willingly added to the pile of presents, and then he crouched down in the canoe, and the hazardous journey to the land of the Hurons began.

After a few days Father Jean began to help paddle, struggling now against the strong current of the Ottawa River. At night his muscles ached so that he was glad to lie down on the hard earth.

When they had to cross on land through the forests, he carried not only his own luggage but that of others. Both on the river and on land they were in danger from the Iroquois, relentless enemies of the Hurons. And then one day the party came to heavy rapids, foaming torrents of water.

"Echon, we stop here," said the Huron chief solemnly. "Demon live in cave. We give him tobacco."

After elaborate ceremonies and wild chanting and dancing, the Indian chief collected tobacco and emptied it into the waters. Only after this could they proceed.

Occasionally the Indians watched "Echon" out of the corners of their eyes to see if he was jeering at them. But he wanted only to understand these curious copper-colored men with their skins painted and heads shaved to all but a small center shoot of hair. He wanted only to win their confidence so he could teach them the Christian faith. All through the journey he thought about it, crouched uncomfortably in a canoe, gazing at the bronzed backs of the Indians.

82

Finally they paddled out into the smooth waters of Lake Huron. And some ninety miles farther, Father Jean saw at last the place he had dreamed so long about. There, before him, at the head of a little bay, was a hill atop which was the Huron village of Toanché. He clambered out of the canoe, and, as Indians from the village gathered around him, he knelt on the shining sand and thanked God for a safe arrival.

He received a friendly welcome, for on the trip he had shown himself "a good Indian" by carrying his own load. Here in Toanché he built his first mission.

Many difficulties awaited him. When no rain fell, the Indians blamed the red cross on the mission. "Thunderbird not like red," they said. When he tried to speak to them of God, he found there was no word in their language he could use. So with much effort he compiled a Huron dictionary.

In all, Father Jean lived and worked among the Hurons for nineteen years. No other missionary has labored more devoutly, nor sacrificed his life more nobly than Father Jean did for these people he loved.

In Canada today there is a college named for him, and streets in the large cities bear his name, also. His statue stands in a niche over the entrance to Parliament in Quebec. And even in England a small church installed a window in the memory of the black-robed giant.

Because he was close to the Indians, he wrote a beautiful carol explaining the Nativity in a way they could understand. He pictured the Infant Jesus wrapped in "rabbit skin," no less holy than in swaddling clothes in a manger.

Stick to the Notes, You Young Rascal

Italian Hymn (Trinity)
Felice de Giardini, 1716-1796

Anonymous

Come Thou Al - might - y King, Help us Thy

Name to sing, Help us to praise! Fa - ther all-

Glo - ri - ous, O'er all vic - to - ri - ous.

Come and reign o - ver us, An - cient of Days.

No one has been able to discover who wrote the words to "Come, Thou Almighty King," one of the favorite hymns of many churches.

We're told it was printed in a little pamphlet, along with one other hymn, and sold in England about two hundred years ago for a copper halfpenny.

At first, people sang it to the tune we use for "My Country 'Tis of Thee." But quite soon it was set to the music of an Italian composer who wrote the melody we sing today.

His name was Felice de Giardini. He wasn't a deeply religious man, but he was so versatile a composer he could write many different kinds of music equally well. He is remembered for operas, string quartets, sonatas, and the music to this fine hymn.

He is remembered, too, for the hubbub he created when he was twenty-one and playing the violin in the handsome new opera house of Naples. In after years he told about it.

Once upon a time—the time was the year 1737—there was an Italian composer by the name of Niccolo Jommelli. He had written an opera that was being sung at the beautiful new San Carlo Opera House in the seaport city of Naples. This was the first season the opera house was open.

Niccolo Jommelli was overjoyed at his stroke of good fortune. He was still a young man, and yet every evening richly dressed men and women came to hear his music. As the curtain fell on each act, they clapped their hands and called, "Bravo! Bravo!" Jommelli's heart pounded within him.

But Jommelli was not the only one who liked applause! There was someone else, a young musician in the orchestra, who enjoyed taking a low, sweeping bow as he glanced upward at the noblemen and their elegant ladies in the boxes of the opera house. He was a violinist named Felice de Giardini. He was a real thorn in the flesh to composer Jommelli, as well as to the entire orchestra.

"Please, Maestro," begged the conductor of the orchestra, "can't you do something about that young scamp who seizes every chance to show off his skill by playing all manner of fancy notes not in the score at all?"

"I know, I know," answered the composer Jommelli. "On opening night he behaved himself quite well and only played the notes I had written for him. But three times since then I have heard him, and have squirmed in my seat. In the accompaniment of one of the airs, he introduced a whole lot of runs on his violin, and with such bravado the countesses went wild. That insufferable upstart took more bows than I did!"

"The trouble is," composer Jommelli added thoughtfully, "he

plays brilliantly! But even so, we cannot tolerate this. Last evening he interrupted so long that he delayed the prima donna, and she left the theater in a most unpleasant temper."

Obviously something had to be done. Jommelli made up his mind to teach young Felice de Giardini, the violinist, a lesson the very next evening.

Backstage, the chorus was preparing for the opening scene. Costumes were hurriedly being put on, makeup applied, wigs fitted securely in place. Down in the front of the theater, the musicians were tuning their instruments, with the low strumming that told the audience the opera was about to begin.

Just as the overture finished and the curtain went up, Jommelli, the composer, slipped into a seat beside Giardini, the violinist.

All went well for a while. Then they came to a part of the opera where the voices of the singers were stilled, and the orchestra played a soft, sad melody. In the midst of it Giardini tucked his violin under his chin and played long, breath-taking cadenzas, a flourish difficult to execute.

He displayed an amazing technique. His violin gave forth a vibrant tone. But not one note of what he was playing was on the sheet of music in front of him.

Just as he finished, Jommelli stood up. With one quick movement, he boxed the ears of the young, clever show-off, and warned, "Stick to the notes, you young rascal!" Giardini sank in his chair, for once not making a sound!

In later years, when Felice de Giardini was a renowned composer himself, he told this story many times, always adding, "I never had a better lesson!"

Although he learned an important lesson in this fashion, he became a master musician by studying with the finest teachers.

After becoming known in Italy, Giardini went to England. He was popular immediately and for nearly forty years conducted Italian opera in London.

For a time he was chamber musician to the Duke of Gloucester and the Duke of Cumberland, which is to say he wrote music and played for their households. In England he became acquainted with a wealthy countess who was devoting herself and her money to establishing churches. She asked him to compose some church music.

The majestic words of "Come, Thou Almighty King" are set to Giardini's impressive notes, quite different from the ones he played, in youthful high spirits, on his violin long before, in the San Carlo Opera House.

Loyal
to the Last

Dennis

HANS G. NÄGELI, 1768-1836
Arr. LOWELL MASON, 1792-1872

JOHN FAWCETT, 1740-1817

Blest be the tie that binds

Our hearts in Chris - tian love:

The fel - low - ship of kin - dred

minds Is like to that a - bove.

Loyalty is one of the wonderful words in the English language. It is one of the finest qualities anyone can possess.

Loyalty is one of the first lessons we learn in life. By the time we are in the first grade we know what it means to be loyal to our families, our friends, our school, and our country.

But the happiest thing about loyalty is that it can work two ways. When we are devoted and loyal, others are devoted and loyal to us.

This is beautifully illustrated in the following story of a great but modest man who, because of his sense of loyalty, made a difficult sacrifice. Yet, it was said of him that "his ministry was greatly prized as was his holy affection—his love and truth."

Susannah Fawcett sat down on a packing case and began to cry. The last of six wagons was being loaded with the Fawcett's furniture, books, pictures, and mementoes of eight years spent among the poor but appreciative people of Wainsgate.

Now the Rev. Fawcett and his family were going to a bigger and more important church located in London, the largest city in the world. Rev. Fawcett had accepted the call to the church. And he had preached his farewell sermon at Wainsgate.

The tears continued to roll down Susannah Fawcett's face. Suddenly her husband sat down beside her on the packing case, and he, too, though he was a dignified man, broke down and wept.

"John, John, I cannot bear this," she said, her voice shaking with sorrow. "I know not how to go!"

"Nor I, neither," replied John Fawcett, "nor will we go."

He called to a boy carrying an armful of their belongings.

"Unload the wagons; put everything in the place where it was before!" The words rang out and reached the people of Wainsgate who had clustered around in mournful groups. Quickly they rushed into the empty house with shouts of joy. Rev. Fawcett was going to stay with them. How would they ever repay his loyalty?

That evening Susannah and John concentrated on writing a letter to the church in London, explaining why they couldn't come after all. It was hard to find the right words.

Just the evening before, Rev. Fawcett and his wife had sat at that table and figured their accounts. It had been quite enticing to think about going to London. The little Baptist church had paid them less than two hundred dollars a year, not nearly enough for the needs of the family. A larger income and greater opportunity had looked most inviting.

But deep within John Fawcett and his wife there was a loyalty that wouldn't let them leave the little church they had come to love. Some way they would get along on the meager salary, as they had before.

When the furniture was all back in place, and the household had settled down again to a very simple life, Rev. Fawcett wrote a hymn that told how he felt. The hymn was "Blest Be the Tie That Binds." In it he expressed the idea that Christians on earth share one another's prayers, hopes, and fears. This binds them together in a spirit of love just as Christians in heaven are held together in a spirit of love.

In later years other honors came to Rev. Fawcett which he also declined because he wanted to stay in Wainsgate. God had blessed his labors there, he said. He did a great deal of writing, and one piece of his, "An Essay on Anger," won the admiration of the king, who wanted to bestow some special benefit.

John Fawcett wanted no favors from anyone, he said, "not even a king." The time came, though, when Rev. Fawcett was glad to accept the offer of a favor from the king. This was when a young friend was sentenced to death for forgery. Rev. Fawcett asked for a pardon and received it.

He enjoyed hymns and commented, "If the Lord has given man the ability to cause such melodious sounds and voices on earth, what delightful harmony will there be in heaven!"

A Christmas Pageant
at Black Cloister

MARTIN LUTHER, 1483-1546
Tr. CATHERINE WINKWORTH, 1829-1878

Vom Himmel Hoch
From VALENTIN SCHUMANN'S
Geistliche Lieder, 1539

From heaven a - bove to earth I come To

bear good news to ev - ery home; Glad

ti - dings of great joy I bring, Where-

of I now will say and sing.

A poor German student who sang for his bread in the streets before the homes of wealthy families grew up to be not only one of the strong forces in the history of the church, but also in the music of the church.

When he was a youth, walking along a country road, a sudden flash of lightning threw him to the ground. He was so terribly frightened, he vowed if he were saved he would give his life to God.

His service to God, and to the church, made him the center of some of the most violent controversies of his time. His hymn which we all know, "A Mighty Fortress Is Our God," was sung throughout Germany during the Reformation.

Yet there was another side to this dynamic man, Martin Luther, as shown by a glimpse into his home on Christmas Eve.

97

"And now, Herr Doktor, what have you in mind for Christmas Eve this year? As though it's not enough for us to feed and clothe our own children and our nieces and nephews, without entertaining them as well! You, with your singing and accompanying on the lute, and your love for theatricals! What have you up your scholarly sleeve?"

Before giving Martin Luther a chance to answer, his wife, Katherine, took a quick breath and continued, "And have you thought of midnight supper? It might have been a good one if you were not always opening our larder to anyone who knocks at our door with a sorry tale. Furthermore," she sputtered, "you would not be so openhanded with our foodstuffs if it were you, Herr Doktor, who took care of the barnyard, and the cows, the fishpond, and the orchard."

Martin Luther laughed. He was used to his wife's good-natured scolding.

"Katie," he said, "I know it isn't easy to manage me as well as all of the children, to say nothing of the students who flock here to meals. But I have a feeling you enjoy setting a table for twenty or twenty-five more than you would enjoy setting for only one, two, or three. And I know you believe, as I do, that Christmas should be a time of happiness."

Katie smiled. "Of course, you're right," she answered.

"Of course!" Martin Luther repeated. "How could we be cold and indifferent to the joy of Christmas, for it is the great gift."

And so Christmas was a festive time in the large stone building (called Black Cloister) at Wittenberg, Germany.

Dr. Luther realized that there were some who thought he was

too gay sometimes. But he realized, too, that Katie and the children loved the pageants and singing he always planned for their holiday.

For this Christmas Eve of 1534, the short, sturdy professor composed a song. When the family and guests were all seated, a man appeared, robed in white to represent an angel.

In a rich voice he sang, "From heaven high I come to you," and continued through a second and third verse, proclaiming how "For you a little child is born," and "He will be your Saviour strong."

Then it was the children's turn. As a chorus they sang, in

German, of course, the response: "Now let us all right merry be," through several stanzas, one of which went:

"Ah, dearest Jesus, be my guest;
　Soft be the bed where thou wilt rest
　A little shrine within my heart,
　That thou and I may never part."

Afterwards, there was bread and cheese, fruit and nuts, and merry talk. Martin Luther played his lute and sang some other songs that he had composed.

He was an unusual writer of hymns in that he could supply the tune for the hymn as well as the words.

"I always loved music," he said one time, "and would not be without the little skill I possess in this art."

Seeing him happy and singing with his family Christmas Eve, one might not have guessed how hard his own childhood had been. The son of a poor miner, he had walked fifty miles to enter school when he was only fourteen.

One might not have thought of him as the brilliant scholar or fearless priest who broke away from his church because he didn't like certain things that were done.

His writings, for which he never took a

100

penny, were published and distributed throughout Germany. They won him many followers.

Above everything, he wished to help his people understand their religion, so he translated the Bible (before then written in Latin) into German. He also wrote songs in German for the people to sing.

He believed hymns should be musical. "Why should the devil," he would ask jokingly, "have all the good tunes?" And so there were new songs for the people to sing to the glory of God, and for his family to enjoy on Christmas Eve.

The Winner
of the School Prize

Reginald Heber, 1783-1826

Nicaea

John B. Dykes, 1823-1876

Ho - ly, ho - ly ho - ly! Lord God al - might - y!

Ear - ly in the morn - ing our song shall rise to Thee;

Ho - ly, ho - ly, ho ly, mer - ci - ful and might - y!

God in Three Per - sons, bless - ed Trin - i - ty.

There is an old saying, "The boy is father to the man," which means that the disposition and character of a boy indicate the kind of man he will grow up to be.

Often this proves to be true. A boy who is earnest and considerate and kind usually turns out to be just that sort of a grown man.

Reginald Heber, when he was no more than three, told his mother not to be afraid in a terrifying storm. Little as he was, he comforted her with his childlike faith.

His loving, comforting spirit never changed to the end of his life.

"May I congratulate you, sir? This is a day on which any parent would be proud," said an admiring Oxford student as he led the elderly Rev. Reginald Heber and his wife to their seats in the Sheldonian Theater. It was a spring day in 1802.

Heads turned in that section of the large, historic theater in the university city of Oxford, England. There was a little buzz of comment:

"It's his parents. His father is lord of the manor and patron of two rectories. But, he'll never forget this day."

"Nor his son, either."

"Nor the University, because young Heber, at twenty, has written a poem for all time."

Then there was a soft "ssshh" as a pale young man with a high forehead stepped onto the platform and faced an audience of fifteen hundred persons who had come to hear him recite his prize-winning poem, "Palestine."

You could have heard a pin drop as the young man began to speak the lines he had written. His gestures were animated. Together with his rich voice, they caught the attention of all the people, who sat motionless lest they miss a word.

When he finished, there was a torrent of applause, and everywhere people murmured, "Yes, it is indeed a poem for all time."

Friends, schoolmates, and schoolmasters pressed toward the platform just to shake the hand of young Reginald Heber. But he was nowhere to be found.

At last he was found in his own room, on his knees, offering a prayer of thankfulness. He was thankful not because of the great honor his poem had earned, but because he had been able to bring joy to his parents. This meant far more than the school prize.

Sometime later he was ordained a minister in the Church of England. After this he wrote several beautiful hymns. He was greatly interested in hymns which pertained to special days of the church year. His "Holy, Holy, Holy" is a Trinity hymn.

When he was raised to the high position of bishop of Calcutta, he went to India to live. This meant leaving his friends and his country, but a diary he kept on shipboard revealed him as the same kind of person he had been as a small boy—protecting and loving. His chief concern was what he could do for the people of India, to whom he was going to minister in the service of the church.

Through a Prison Window

THEODULPH of ORLEANS C. 820
Tr. JOHN M. NEALE, 1818-1866

Valet Will Ich Dir Geben
MELCHOIR TESCHNER, 1613

All glo-ry, laud, and hon-or, To Thee, Re-deem-er, King,

To whom the lips of chil-dren made sweet ho-san-nas ring.

Thou art the King of Is-ra-el, Thou Da-vid's roy-al Son.

Who in the Lord's name com-est, the King and Bless-ed One.

On the right bank of the Loire River, in the heart of France, is situated the ancient city of Orleans. Through many centuries important things have happened there.

Before the birth of Christ, Julius Caesar, a Roman general, burned the city. Three hundred years afterwards it was rebuilt by a Roman emperor, Aurelian, who gave the city his name, later changed to Orleans.

In 1429 Orleans was the center of a bitter war, between the French and British. If the city had been lost by the French, all of France might have been ruled by the British. The French army, led by a peasant girl, Joan of Arc, fought off the enemy and saved the country. After that, Joan of Arc was called "The Maid of Orleans."

Our story of Orleans is the story of Theodulph. It takes us back to the reign of Emperor Charlemagne, eleven hundred years ago. To be bishop of Orleans, then, was an achievement which many would have liked to realize.

"So Charlemagne is bringing a new bishop all the way from a little monastery in Florence," complained one of the clergy who envied Theodulph his good fortune.

"It's because Theodulph comes of a noble family," said another sarcastically.

"More likely it's because he can write poetry," commented a third. "Charlemagne, not having had much education himself, is a great one for learning. Not long ago he pardoned a murderer. And why? Charlemagne liked the rogue's verse!"

The three laughed scornfully as another joined the group and added his opinion. "Charlemagne is studying Latin, I hear. I also hear he is determined his bishops shall establish reading schools."

So, perhaps, the fact that Theodulph had a reputation as a writer and a poet had a great deal to do with his suddenly being invited to come to France as the Bishop of Orleans. It was an appointment he was overjoyed to accept. He could picture to himself how wonderful it would be to have the company of the learned men who clustered around the court, some of them poets like himself.

"I shall be a help to Charlemagne," he assured himself as he arrived in Orleans. "I am not out of sympathy with the emperor's ideas. I think well of him for encouraging the artists of the realm —goldsmiths and metalworkers and those whose skill turns out all those fine ivory pieces. And I approve of Charlemagne's wisdom in permitting conquered people to keep their own laws. Most of all, I agree that the priests are not as well educated as they should be in theology or in classical literature. And the children of the empire lack schools."

Charlemagne, in turn, approved of Theodulph. In addition

to his regular duties as bishop, Theodulph was named as the king's personal religious adviser.

Theodulph found favor in other parts, also. When the pope was having trouble in Rome trying to convince the people that he was innocent of serious charges brought against him, Theodulph took the pope's part against his accusers. For this, Theodulph came back from Rome with still another honor: he was allowed to wear the pallium, a white circular band of wool over his outer vestments —a privilege the pope alone could grant.

Later, on a Christmas Day, in the great church of St. Peter's in Rome, the pope crowned Charlemagne emperor before a huge crowd of Roman people.

This pleased Theodulph and made his high position even more secure than it had been.

Yet, somewhat later, Louis, the son of Charlemagne, was to be crowned. Then it was Charlemagne, himself, who put the crown on his son's head.

When Louis became king, disaster began for Theodulph. Louis was not in the least like Charlemagne, his father. Although nick-named, "The Pious," Louis often acted rashly and repented after it was too late to make amends.

When his nephew, then king of Italy, appeared to be heading a revolt, Louis had the young monarch killed. All those suspected of being among his followers were sent to prison. Theodulph was among them.

In due time, Louis was sorry for his cruelty and pardoned some of the suspected followers, but not Theodulph.

The worthy bishop was imprisoned in a monastery. One day

he heard that Louis was going to pass by with all his royal retinue on Easter Sunday.

"With God's help, I shall be his mouthpiece for teaching the king mercy and goodness and humility," Theodulph resolved.

On Easter Sunday, along came the king. With him were his attendants in splendid costumes and equipped with banners. They

made an impressive procession as they passed through the streets of the town.

As the king approached, Theodulph stood by the window of his cell and sang out in a clear voice a hymn he had composed, "All Glory, Laud and Honor." The words warned the king that homage belongs only to the Lord.

111

Some say that Theodulph was promptly pardoned, although it isn't certain. But on Palm Sunday, we sing Theodulph's immortal hymn and hope its beauty softened a king's heart.

The Bandmaster's Son in Royal Velvet

SABINE BARING-GOULD, 1834-1924

St. Gertrude
ARTHUR S. SULLIVAN, 1842-1900

On - ward, Chris-tian sol - diers! March-ing as to war,

With the cross of Je - sus Go - ing on be - fore.

Christ the roy - al Mas - ter Leads a - gainst the foe;

For-ward in - to bat - tle, See His ban - ners go!

REFRAIN

On-ward, Christian Sol - diers, Marching as to war,

With the cross of Je - sus Go - ing on be - fore.

If you ask your parents who Sir Arthur Sullivan was, they will probably say, "Oh, he's the man who wrote all those gay tunes for light operas, such as 'The Pirates of Penzance' and 'The Mikado,'" and your father might begin to sing:

> "My object all sublime
> I shall achieve in time—
> To let the punishment fit the crime. . . .
> The punishment fit the crime!"

Your parents' memories will be exactly right.

Yet, they may not have tucked away the recollection that Sir Arthur Sullivan wrote the music to "Onward, Christian Soldiers," which just about everybody can sing.

He wrote a whole lot of other things, too, and was a most popular person. Other people sought him because they enjoyed his company. An attractive, delightful man, he was spared the hard struggle of his father in the musical world, as we shall see.

114

Thomas Sullivan bounded up the five steps to the front door of No. 8 Bolwell Terrace. Usually he walked up heavily, after his long evening of playing the clarionet in the orchestra of the Surrey Theater in London, where he lived.

Now his heart was as light as his footsteps.

"Maria, Maria," he called. "Come! I have good news for us."

His wife hurried to him.

"What is it, Thomas?"

"What *is* it?" he teasingly repeated. "It's the coming of a new day, that's what is is. I've been appointed bandmaster at the Royal Military College. This means it will not be so hard to set aside twenty pounds a year to pay for this house in which to live."

His wife took his hand affectionately. "And it means," she said joyously, "that you will not have to stay awake all hours of the night, copying music to earn a few extra pounds for food for our children."

She looked down thoughtfully on their two small sons, Frederick and Arthur. "Perhaps," she said slowly, "one of them may turn out to be a musician."

Thomas Sullivan's good-natured Irish face was a mixture of hope and despair as he answered, "In one way I'd like it, but in another, I'd not want it. As you know so well, Maria, there's a bare living in it."

Thomas Sullivan was an excellent musician; and he was acquainted with military life because his father had been a soldier. As a result, he was immediately successful as bandmaster at the Royal Military College.

With the fortunes of the family so much improved, everyone

was happy. Arthur was especially happy about his father's new position because it gave him a chance to see and touch and try all of the instruments in the band. By the time he was eight, he could play every different instrument. And he could also write music. He composed an anthem, "By the Waters of Babylon."

When Thomas Sullivan saw the anthem he decided, although his income was still not large, to send his son to a private school where his talent for music could develop.

Arthur was a good student. He put his heart in everything he did. Soon he was eager to buy a piano; but the cost was too much and he couldn't.

Next he began sending letters home asking if he couldn't, please, join the choir of the Chapel Royal. This was a group of singers trained especially to sing in the chapel in the palace of the king of England. Arthur Sullivan loved singing.

"It means everything to me," he wrote his father, who, after thinking the matter over carefully, gave his consent. Young Arthur, then twelve years old, was accepted for the Chapel choir.

His voice was high and pure, so he was selected to sing solos on several occasions. He even sang before the queen.

Because his musical ability was quickly recognized, he won first one scholarship for more studies and then another. Because of his astonishing knowledge of music, he attracted much attention, especially when at twenty years of age he wrote the music for a production of Shakespeare's play, "The Tempest."

Unmistakably, Arthur Sullivan was on his way to fame and fortune.

He became an organist at a London church, and a professor

of music at the Royal Academy. And then he began to write the music for light operas, music for which he was knighted by the Queen in 1883.

Because he was distinguished and had many friends, he was often invited to visit people. One time he spent a few days with friends who had a country house with a chapel and organ in it. His hosts showed him some verses written by an English clergyman, Sabine Baring-Gould, for a processional of schoolboys.

Suddenly Arthur Sullivan's thoughts raced back to his boyhood home, when as a lad he explored the instruments in his father's military band.

He sat down and wrote the spirited music to the hymn which some critics called the "greatest marching song in the world," "Onward, Christian Soldiers."

The Thankful Heart

Nun Danket
JOHANN CRÜGER, 1598-1662
Harmonized
FELIX MENDELSSOHN, 1809- 1847

MARTIN RINKART, 1586-1649
Tr. CATHERINE WINKWORTH, 1829-1878

Now thank we all our God With heart and hands and voic-es,

Who won-drous things hath done, In whom His world re-joic-es;

Who, from our moth-ers' arms, Hath blessed us on our way

With count-less gifts of love, And still is ours to-day.

Thanks
With hearts
and hands
and voices

We all find it easy to give thanks when we are surrounded with blessings.

When there is peace in our land, when those dear to us are in good health and happy, when tomorrow looks promising and today all is well, who wouldn't be thankful!

Yet, now and then we discover the rare person who has no outward cause for thankfulness, but who, nevertheless, treasures within his heart God's "countless gifts of love."

Martin Rinkart, born in the late 16th century, was like that.

"We have a candidate for the post of deacon in our city," announced the head of the town council of Eilenburg, Germany. "Possibly some of you may remember him: Martin Rinkart. He was born here; his father, I believe, was a barrel-maker."

"I remember him," said another member of the council. "They were quite poor. I think the boy went to St. Thomas School in Leipzig as a free scholar and chorister and then was given a scholarship to the University."

"That is correct," said the head of the council, holding a letter of application. "He studied for the ministry, and supported himself, he says, by his musical skill. I suggest we recommend the young man's appointment."

The appointment would have been good news to Martin Rinkart, who as a little boy in his father's cooper's shop had dreamed of going to a great university and becoming a pastor. Unfortunately, he didn't get the appointment, because the most important churchman in Eilenburg objected, saying, "Rinkart is a better musician than clergyman."

And so the son of the barrel-maker waited seven years to be welcomed back to his birthplace. This time, the town council invited him to become the archdeacon, and there were no objections.

Every day, for the rest of his life, Martin Rinkart proved how completely wrong the people had been who thought he wouldn't make a good minister. Although he did write fine hymns, he also served God as faithfully and selflessly as any pastor ever has done.

Throughout a terrible war in Europe which lasted thirty years, he devoted himself to his people. Eilenburg was a walled city, and so it became a refuge for fugitives who came from miles around.

It grew so overcrowded there were dreadful epidemics and a severe lack of food.

Rev. Rinkart was the only minister there for a long period of time. He alone had to bury the many, many dead, comfort all the grieving, share his meager supply of food, and look after the families in his church.

Much as he was needed, his faithful people urged him at times to leave for just a little while. "The rest of the clergy are not so unsparing of themselves," they said to him. "We seem to remember one churchman who went off for a holiday when the pestilence was at its worst."

Yet he would not leave. Resolutely he remained in his city, helping as best he could throughout the entire thirty years. During all those years he did his best to keep up the people's courage and their faith in God.

"Rev. Rinkart is our only hope," the people said when a Swedish army officer demanded a sum of money from the citizens of Eilenburg which they could not pay. So the earnest minister went to the Swedish officer and pleaded for them. Martin Rinkart came back filled with sadness. "We cannot hope for much," he said, "but we can pray. Let us gather together and ask God's help." The prayers were answered, and new terms were offered, which the people could meet.

Again they gathered for prayers, this time to give thanks. No one ever understood how Rev. Rinkart, who had lived through so many tragedies, could keep such a spirit of thanksgiving. His triumphant hymn, "Now Thank We All Our God," was written looking forward to the day peace would come. And when at last it did come, the hymn was sung after the signing of the peace treaty. It has been used on a great many occasions since then when men's hearts were devoutly thankful.

The Friar Who Found God

SYDNEY H. NICHOLSON, 1875-

Lytlington
From Sarum Primer, 1558

Very Slow

God be in my head, and in my un - der-stand - ing;

God be in mine eyes, and in my look - ing;

God be in my mouth, and in my speak - ing;

God be in my heart, and in my think - ing;

God be at mine end, and at my de - part - ing.

Printed by permission of the Royal School of Church
Music, Addington Palace, Croydon, Surrey, England

In England, many years ago, there was an ancient town called Old Sarum where there was a beautiful cathedral and where there was a bishop's palace.

In time, the old cathedral was torn down, and much of it was used to build a handsome new cathedral in the valley of the Avon River. Another town grew up around the new cathedral, called New Sarum. The bishop moved there.

From time to time books of English hymns appeared which had been printed by the order of the bishop of Sarum. They were called Sarum Primers, and they contained only the verses of hymns, not the music.

In one of these early Sarum primers, the quiet, thoughtful hymn, "God Be in My Head," was included. It wasn't signed by any name, and no one knows who the author of it was. It seems fairly certain that it had been used for many years before it was published and had been part of daily devotions. It means just as much to us today as it did to others long ago, but during the reign of Henry VIII it had a special application.

125

A friar, in his brown habit and white mantle, walked slowly along the garden path. Here were the shrubs in long, regular rows. Here were the trees planted with an eye to beauty. And here were the red and white roses which often he had picked to decorate the plain wood altar. Soon he would be leaving it all.

He was joined in his evening stroll by another friar, and because both were young and bewildered, they spoke resentfully.

"Before long, we shall be homeless," said Brother John bitterly. "I heard only yesterday that the Carmelites are the next whose houses will be closed."

"I'm afraid so," replied Brother Thomas, "and by a king who calls himself an accomplished scholar! He has forgotten that the monasteries kept the light of learning burning these many years!"

"Why should he want to close this small place?" Brother John interrupted. "We have too little property to fatten the royal purse. Besides there are all the poor people who come to our doors for a daily dole of food. What will they do?"

The two young friars paced the walk in silence, broken at last by Brother John: "Sometimes I wonder just where God is!"

With no more words, they went to prayers; but the next evening they met again beside the neat hedges and talked.

"Where can we find God?" Brother John asked, coming back to his question of the night before. "Was he with the king when he traveled to meet Francis I of France, with so many attendants they devoured two thousand sheep in one month?"

Brother John dug the toe of his sandal into the garden path and continued, "Is he with the rich and powerful Cardinal Wolsey? Where are we to find God?" His face was troubled.

"Ah well," Brother Thomas consoled him, "I understand we shall receive pensions from the state, and so we'll not be turned into the road. But I, like you, feel lost and far away from our Lord."

That night Brother John lay awake on his cot in the plain cell he occupied and once more asked, "Where can we find God?" Suddenly a prayer that he had been saying daily came to him, almost as though it were written on the wall. He knelt down beside a little altar in the corner of his cell and began to say the words, interpreting softly to himself:

"God be in my head, and in my understanding";

(*"When I bow my head, may Thy loving spirit enter into it; then, I'll ask not to be understood, but to understand."*)

"God be in mine eyes, and in my looking;"

(*"May my eyes seek not the evil, but look*

always for traces of Thy handiwork in Thy great
universe.")
"God be in my mouth, and in my speaking";
("Guard my lips from falsehood, dear Lord, and
unkindness, and blasphemy.")
"God be in my heart, and in my thinking";
("So the meditations of my heart may be acceptable
in thy sight.")
"God be at mine end, and at my departing."
("I shall fear no evil, for thou art with me.")

A wonderfully sweet peace stole into the heart of Brother John.
Within himself he had found God.